Dedicated to Liona's late cat, Muffin, who lived to be almost twenty.

The Cat Who Played Guitar
Liona Boyd
Published by Moston Productions
Illustrations by Laura Fernandez and Rick Jacobson

lionaboyd.com

Illustration and Design by Jacobson Fernandez

ISBN: 978-1-7773394-2-5

First Edition: October 2022

The Cat Who Played Guitar

Liona Boyd
© 2022 Moston Productions

THIS IS THE STORY
TOLD WIDE AND TOLD FAR
OF A BEAUTIFUL CAT
WHO COULD PLAY THE GUITAR

HE HAD EMERALD EYES
AND SOFT SILKY FUR
WHEN HE ZOOMED THROUGH THE HOUSE
ALL YOU SAW WAS A BLUR

MUFFIN'S OWNER, LIONA
DRESSED UP LIKE A STAR
BUT WHAT SHE LOVED MOST
WAS TO PLAY THE GUITAR

He jumped in the cases
She let him explore
And chased her guitar strings
Around on the floor

But his owner, Liona
Was often not home
And those days poor Muffin
Felt sad and alone

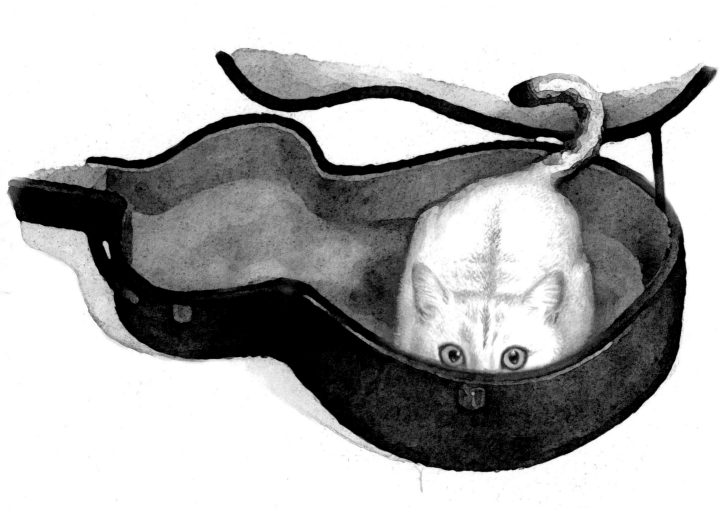

MUFFIN TOOK LITTLE CAT NAPS
HE SLEPT EVERYWHERE
AND LAZED IN THE SUN
ON HIS FAVOURITE CHAIR

THEN ONE DAY SHE CAME BACK
FROM TRAVELING FAR
AND UNPACKED A MINIATURE
SPANISH GUITAR

It smelled of the forest
And sweet, flowery wood
How he'd love to play it!
If only he could

She took it and put it
Beneath the back stairs
In a closet where she'd stored
Her old teddy bears

He'd a sudden idea!
He made note of the place
And a secretive smile
Crossed his pussycat face

At night by Liona
Pretending to sleep
He now had a dream
And a secret to keep

He crept down the hall
It was dark, it was night
And the moon on the carpet
Was all that was light

The room wasn't far
And the door was ajar
And there on a shelf
Lay the tiny guitar!

He used his clipped claws
To pluck every string
The way he'd seen Liona
Make her guitar sing

Muffin played and he played
'Til his paws became sore
Then he carried it back
And his nose shut the door

Each night in the closet
For hours he stayed
And taught himself pieces
Liona had played

But one cloudy morning
She had to depart
And Muffin felt lonely
And sad in his heart

The Queen and Prince Philip
Had asked her to play
A concert in England
And she'd flown away

He'd seen her on TV
She mentioned his name
But life for poor Muffin
Just wasn't the same

THEN ONE HAPPY EVENING
SHE BURST THROUGH THE DOOR
MUFFIN GOT SO EXCITED
HE SLID ON THE FLOOR!

HE WENT TO THE KITCHEN
AND MEOWED "LET US EAT"
SO SHE COOKED HIM SOME SHRIMP
HIS MOST FAVOURITE TREAT

HE HEARD A LOUD SHRIEK
AND HE DIDN'T KNOW WHY
SHE'D DROPPED A HOT PLATE
AND HAD STARTED TO CRY

HER FINGERS WERE BURNED,
AND HIS DINNER GONE "SPLAT!".
SO HE GAVE HER A LEG RUB
'CAUSE HE WAS A CAT

Now Muffin felt badly
But grinned ear to ear
'Cause now he could show her his
Brilliant idea

He ran to the closet
And soon he returned
To play for her
Some of the pieces he'd learned

Liona was speechless
Her eyes shone like stars
She knew very well
That cats don't play guitars!

She hugged him and kissed him
So much he was sore
Her next concert was saved!
So she hugged him some more

She sewed a tuxedo
With rhinestones so bright
Black velvet, gold buttons
It fit him just right

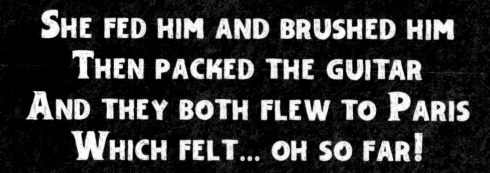

She fed him and brushed him
Then packed the guitar
And they both flew to Paris
Which felt... oh so far!

Next night all the people
Let out a big cheer,
They had come to hear Liona
And had no idea

THAT A BEAUTIFUL CAT
WHO HAD TRAVELED SO FAR
WOULD STRIDE ON THE STAGE
WITH A TINY GUITAR

AND NOBODY THERE
COULD BELIEVE THEIR OWN EYES
ENCHANTED AND SPELLBOUND
THEY GASPED WITH SURPRISE

The crowd clapped like crazy
The critics went mad
Muffin bowed and meowed
'Twas the best fun he'd had

He took four final bows
Then he jumped off his chair
'Cause behind the thick curtains
Liona was there

He leapt to her arms
They twirled 'round and around
As the clapping continued
Its thunderous sound

Yes music makes magic
Though easy it seems
We have to work hard
For impossible dreams

Now they travel the world
And they play all day long
And Muffin is famous
From Rome to Hong Kong

A cat, fancy that!
So wherever you are
Remember the cat
Who could play the guitar ~

To see a music video with Liona and Muffin,
(before he had learned to play the guitar),
scan the code below.

About the author

LIONA BOYD

Liona Boyd has always loved animals, and particularly cats, since she lived as a child in England. Liona is an internationally acclaimed classical guitarist and singer known as "The First Lady of the Guitar". She has received five Juno Awards, five honorary doctorates, Officer of the Order of Canada, The Order of Ontario, and three Lifetime Achievement awards in the USA.

Liona has recorded twenty-nine albums, many of which are Gold and Platinum, distributed by Universal Music. She has composed much of her own repertoire. Liona performed solo classical guitar and orchestral concerts around the world, gave private concerts for dozens of heads of state, including the US President and British Royal Family, was a guest three times on The Tonight Show with Johnny Carson and has had her own TV specials, including A Winter Fantasy that was broadcast by PBS and streamed on CBC's Gem. Liona wrote two bestselling autobiographies, the first of which she also recorded as an audiobook.

In addition to her classical career Liona is an accomplished songwriter who enjoys writing poetry, and you can find many of her music videos on YouTube.

Liona Boyd with Queen Elizabeth and HRH Prince Philip

Muffin in Concert